R2-D2

GALACTIC HERO

BY BENJAMIN HARPER

STERLING INNOVATION
New York

An Imprint of Sterling Publishing Co., Inc.
1166 Avenue of the Americas
New York, NY 10036

This book is part of the *STAR WARS: BUILD R2-D2* kit and is not to be sold separately.

ISBN 978-1-4351-4604-4

For information about custom editions, special sales, and premium and corporate purchases, please contact Sterling Special Sales at 800-805-5489 or specialsales@sterlingpublishing.com.

Manufactured in China
4 6 8 10 9 7 5
www.sterlingpublishing.com

Visit the official Star Wars website at:
www.starwars.com

Designer: Sam Dawson
Editor: Delia Greve
Photo Researcher: Emily Zach
Product Developer: Peter Schumacher
Production Coordinator: Tom Miller
Managing Editor: Michael del Rosario

Special thanks to Carol Roeder, Jonathan Rinzler, Troy Alders, and Leland Chee at LucasBooks.

CONTENTS

HUMBLE BEGINNINGS

In a galaxy of Jedi, Sith, bounty hunters, and countless civilizations and species, the actions of lowly droids are rarely taken into account. From protocol droids to mouse droids and massive droid armies, these machines are designed to do menial tasks. It is rare that a droid is recognized and even rarer that it is rewarded for its services.

Long before the formation of the Rebel Alliance, the galaxy was struggling. Dark forces vowed to overthrow the long-standing Republic and to launch the once-peaceful galaxy into bitter civil war. From the start of this struggle, one droid went above and beyond his humble call of duty in order to fight for his friends and for what he knew was right—that droid was R2-D2.

If R2-D2 had failed at any of his missions, or hadn't acted on his own initiative many times, the galaxy would have been a different place. Queen Amidala wouldn't have escaped from Naboo; Luke Skywalker wouldn't have received his Jedi training from Obi-Wan Kenobi; Princess Leia would be Darth Vader's prisoner; and the Death Star would have brought a reign of incomparable terror to the galaxy.

Many heroes in the galaxy respected R2-D2 and trusted him with vital missions. They knew he would do whatever it took to accomplish the task at hand, and that he possessed a level of bravery few living beings could claim.

R2-D2's illustrious, galaxy-saving career began in the Outer Rim on the verdant planet Naboo. There he served under King Veruna, Naboo's leader before Queen Amidala, as an anonymous worker droid. Eventually he was assigned to the Royal Security Forces and accompanied Bravo Squadron on escort missions. It was a time of peace and the missions were routine. When Queen Amidala ascended the throne, R2-D2 was reassigned to the Royal Starship, where he tended to minor repairs. The little droid's path would soon change, however, and he would blast off to greatness.

HERO NOTES

Industrial Automaton

CREATORS OF THE R-SERIES ASTROMECH DROIDS

The massive droid manufacturer Industrial Automaton produces the ever-popular R-series astromech droids. The R-series line launched with the bulky and slightly clunky R1. From this first R droid, the line continued through generations of improvements (and failures—the R5 series was a financial flop and deemed a technical disaster by all critics) to the most recent R9 model. Aside from the R1, the R-series astromech droids have all retained similar structural dimensions, with modifications being made to each generation's internal technology.

MISSION 1

MID-BATTLE REPAIR

LOCATION: **NABOO**

Under the guise of a trade dispute, the Trade Federation places a blockade around the planet Naboo in preparation for planet invasion. Their ever-increasing threat forces the planet's ruler, Queen Amidala, to seek aid from the Galactic Senate, but first she needs to make it off the planet and past the blockade. The queen, along with her handmaidens, security, and two Jedi protectors board her Royal Starship. As the ship blasts away from the planet, the Trade Federation launches an assault.

The Droid Control Ship orbiting the planet showers the tiny starship with heavy blaster fire. Built for diplomatic missions, the Royal Starship holds little firepower to counter the attack. A direct hit knocks out the ship's deflector shields, leaving them completely unprotected. A group of astromech droids spring into action and ascend a repulsorlift tube to the ship's outer hull. Amid continued attacks, the droids attempt to repair the deflector shield.

One by one, the astromechs are blasted off the hull until only one droid remains. Thinking quickly, R2-D2 uses his repair arm to bypass the main power generator, and bring the ship's deflectors back online. The ship blasts past the blockade and away from Naboo.

Once safely away from danger, Queen Amidala calls R2-D2 before her. She commends R2 on his excellent service and orders Padmé, one of her handmaidens, to clean him as a token of her gratitude.

RIGHT: R2-D2 and his fellow astromech droids attempt to repair the Royal Starship mid-battle.

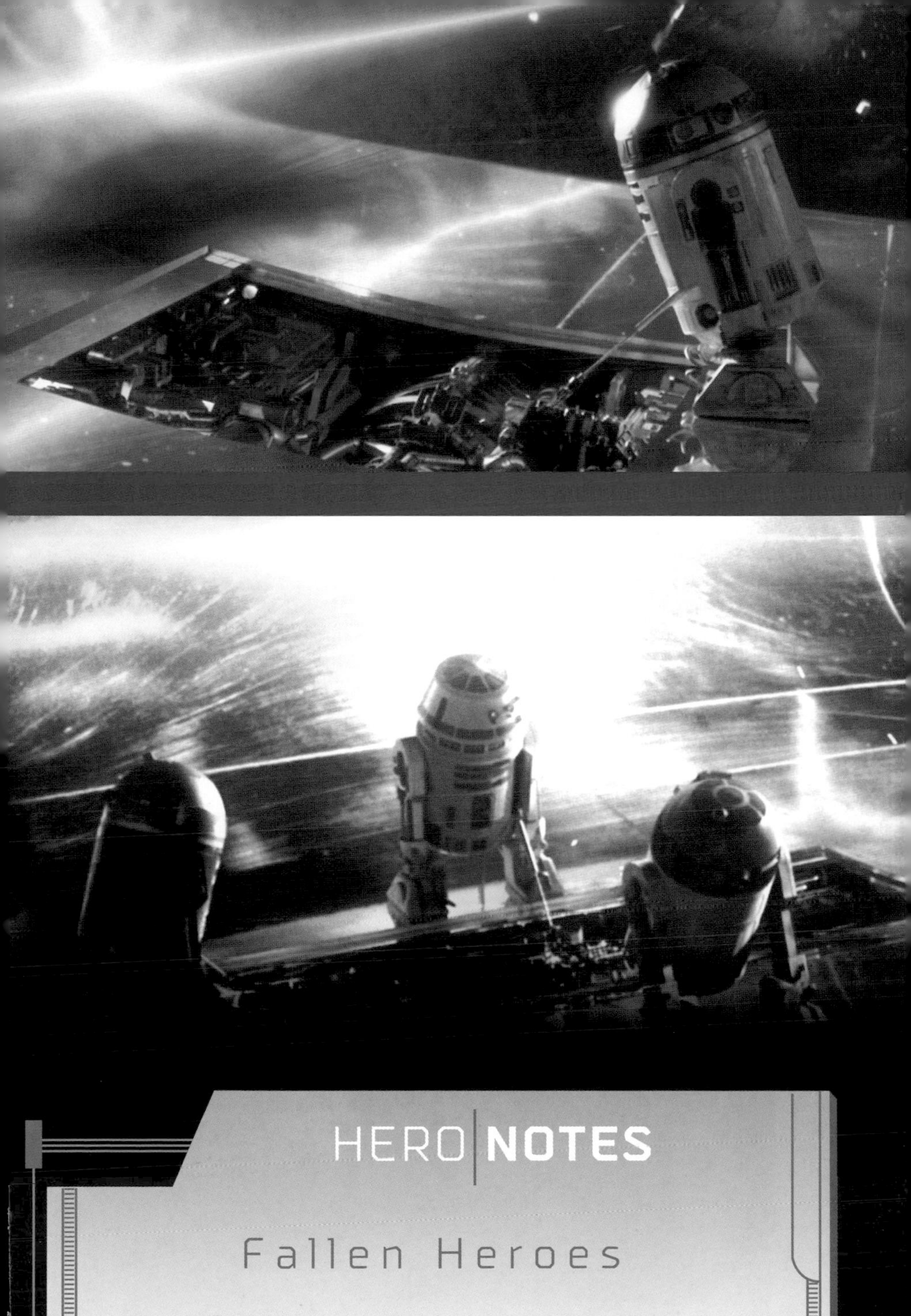

HERO NOTES

Fallen Heroes

Although R2-D2 is commended as the hero, many other astromech droids fall during the daring mission. The droids sacrifice themselves in the line of duty so that the queen might fulfill her mission.

MISSION 2

HELPING ANAKIN FULFILL HIS DESTINY

LOCATION: **MOS ESPA, TATOOINE**

Although R2-D2 repairs the Royal Starship's deflector shield, its hyperdrive is also damaged during the escape from Naboo. To find replacement parts, the ship lands on the remote planet of Tatooine. R2 sets off across the desert with Jedi Master Qui-Gon Jinn and other members of the crew. At a junk shop, they meet a young slave named Anakin. In order to free the child and win the replacement parts they need for the starship, Qui-Gon bets on Anakin to win a Podrace. There is only one problem—Anakin has built his Podracer himself and it doesn't work! R2-D2 and Anakin along with a few others set to work repairing and rebuilding the Podracer for the big race. The droid's technical expertise is just what the broken Podracer needs. R2 uses his built-in mechanical knowledge along with his internal repair components to fix the former scrap pile. When Anakin finally revs the engines, the Podracer roars to life. Anakin wins the race and his freedom, thanks in part to R2-D2. Without his help, the group would not have won the race, nor obtained the parts they needed to repair the Royal Starship. The queen with her retinue leaves Tatooine for Coruscant—and a future that will change the galaxy forever.

ABOVE: R2-D2 hard at work fixing the engines on Anakin's Podracer.

HERO | **NOTES**

Making Friends

When R2 arrives on Tatooine, little does he realize he will meet C-3PO, a protocol droid who will become his near-constant companion for the remainder of his existence. Constructed out of scrounged parts by Anakin Skywalker, the protocol droid is nearly perfect in construction—only one thing is missing. Anakin hasn't yet given him outer plating. C-3PO is, as R2-D2 points out upon their first meeting, "naked." C-3PO, a fidgety droid by nature, is extremely embarrassed!

R2 and C-3PO part on Tatooine, but the two eventually reunite and fight alongside many heroes in countless battles—they become nearly inseparable.

MISSION 3

TAKING DOWN THE CONTROL SHIP

LOCATION: **NABOO SPACE**

After diplomacy fails on Coruscant, Queen Amidala returns to Naboo in order to retake her planet by force. The plan calls for her fleet of N-1 starfighters to destroy the Droid Control Ship while she attempts to capture the Trade Federation leaders.

When the fighting begins, Anakin takes cover aboard one of the fighters, and accidentally triggers the ship, sucking R2-D2 up into the astromech copilot socket. The ship kicks into autopilot, launching the pair into space. R2 orders Anakin to take the ship back to Naboo, but Anakin asks R2 to turn off the ship's autopilot. Amid a fierce space battle, Anakin and R2 work together to maneuver the ship through the swarm of ships surrounding the Droid Control Ship. After taking a glancing hit, the N-1 starfighter spirals out of control and skids into the Control ship's main hangar. There, the starfighter overheats, but Anakin regains control in time to fend off the battle droids closing in on them. A lucky shot misses the droids and hits the control ship's power generator instead, setting off a chain reaction that destroys the ship. Anakin and R2 blast out of the ship's hangar just as it begins to explode. Without the Control ship, the droid armies marching on Naboo shut down. The Trade Federation's hold on Naboo is broken—the battle is won.

LEFT: Anakin and R2 take cover in an N-1 Starfighter.
ABOVE: The Droid Control Ship explodes from the inside out.

HERO NOTES

Sharing Naboo's Secrets

Queen Amidala stores the technical readouts for Theed Palace in R2-D2's memory banks to keep the information safe. When the time comes to plan the attack with the Jedi and her troops, R2 projects a map of the city and the palace, giving the fighters their secret route.

HERO NOTES

Astromechs and Starfighters

Astromechs are built to copilot several smaller fighter ships. A special socket is built into ships to fit these droid units. They enter the craft either from below, or they are lowered into their socket from above. The droid sits behind the pilot's seat, slightly elevated where it is able to see what is going on outside the ship. The vessel's computer and systems plug directly into the droid's body so the two can communicate and help the pilot with navigation and control. Due to this direct link, astromech droids can fly ships themselves when the regular pilot wants to take a rest.

MINI-MISSION
Protect the Senator

LOCATION: **CORUSCANT**

Senator Amidala's political views and the pending vote in the Senate cause an assassination attempt to be made on her life. For her protection, two Jedi are assigned to watch over her along with R2-D2, her loyal droid. To draw out the assassin, Padmé uses herself as bait. It falls to R2 to keep watch over her. He stays by her bed, on full alert, scanning her room continuously for any intruders or irregularities.

Unfortunately, the bounty hunter who had been hired to kill the Senator sends an ASN-121 assassin droid to do her dirty work. It silently cuts a hole in the transparisteel of Padmé's apartment, allowing two deadly kouhouns to sneak in. R2's sensors don't detect the vile creatures. At the last minute, the Jedi race into the room to save the Senator, killing the poisonous creatures.

MISSION 4

RESCUE THE SENATOR

LOCATION: **GEONOSIS DROID FACTORY**

Upon hearing that Obi-Wan Kenobi has been taken captive by the Separatists, Anakin Skywalker and Padmé Amidala fly to Geonosis. They plan to rescue the Jedi Master, but when Anakin and Padmé stumble into a fight with the Geonosians that leads them into the droid factory, it is they who need rescuing.

R2-D2 and C-3PO argue about what to do, but R2 knows Anakin and Padmé need help. R2 wins the argument, and the two droids go in search of their human masters. C-3PO comes to the end of their path—below him is a maze of conveyor belts. R2 insists they dive into action and pushes C-3PO off the ledge. The protocol droid falls onto a conveyor belt and runs into a machine where his head is separated from his body and attached to a battle droid. His body, then, becomes host to a battle droid's head!

Meanwhile, R2 monitors Senator Amidala's movements through the droid factory. She manages to avoid many obstacles, but when she topples into a giant tub destined to be filled with molten metal—she's trapped.

Seeing the Senator's plight, R2 reveals a secret—he can fly! He extends rocket boosters from his outer legs and takes off, soaring through the droid factory. He zooms to a dataport where he plugs into the system, relaying the command to turn the conveyor belt off mere moments before Amidala would have been doused with liquid metal. The vat comes to a stop and drops the Senator to the floor.

LEFT TOP: R2-D2 takes his first flight.
LEFT BOTTOM: Padmé escapes the giant tub, only to face a gang of Geonosians.

HERO | NOTES

The Droid Factory

The droid factory on Geonosis was built by the Techno Union, a member of the Separatist movement. It was conceived to mass-produce battle droids, super battle droids, and droidekas (also known as destroyer droids). The factory is a labyrinth of conveyor belts and antiquated machinery that can assemble and manufacture thousands of droids a day.

HERO | NOTES

First Flight: R2-D2 Takes Off

R2-D2 is equipped with a pair of rocket boosters built by Brooks Propulsion Devices. These booster turbines allow R2 to fly when obstructions inhibit his standard method of movement. He uses them sparingly as they burn fuel rapidly and are easily damaged, though they have come in handy on more than one occasion in his heroic career.

MISSION 5

REPAIR C-3PO

LOCATION: **GEONOSIS ARENA**

C-3PO is in trouble! After his misadventures in the droid factory, the protocol droid' s head and body are separated—and both are marching into battle attached to battle droids! Helpless to override the battle droids' actions, he is forced to fight for the Separatists. His body begins firing on a Jedi, but a lucky rebounded blaster shot knocks the battle droid head off the hapless protocol droid's body. Meanwhile his head is profusely apologizing for firing upon each Jedi. One Jedi takes pity on C-3PO and uses a Force push to knock him over, trapping the battle droid's body.

R2-D2 zigzags through blaster fire and lightsaber battles to rescue his friend. He locates C-3PO's head and uses a powerful suction device located in the rear of his body to remove it from the battle droid's body. Dragging it to C-3PO's body, R2 uses his expert skills to put the fidgety droid back together.

ABOVE: R2-D2 reattaches C-3PO's head mid-battle.

HERO NOTES

Protocol Droids

These prim droids are humanoid in design and are programmed to follow etiquette as well as assist in diplomatic missions. Their translation skills are vital in delicate galactic dealings, and therefore, ambassadors, politicians, and other high-ranking officials use these droids to ensure proper communication with species that speak different languages and have unusual customs.

HERO NOTES

Droids of the Clone Wars

The Separatists' army primarily consists of cheap, mass-produced droids that are more easily replaceable than living troops. The most common models are battle droids, super battle droids, and droidekas. Throughout the Clone Wars, the Separatists develop new models, including dwarf spider droids, tank droids, and deadly hailfire droids.

MISSION 6

BATTLING BUZZ DROIDS

LOCATION: **CORUSCANT SPACE**

The Battle of Coruscant is raging! Obi-Wan Kenobi and Anakin Skywalker maneuver their Jedi Interceptors through enemy troops in order to rescue kidnapped Supreme Chancellor Palpatine. They are assaulted first by vulture droids, then pursued by missiles. R2-D2 takes over and with a bit of clever flying helps Anakin avoid being hit. The missiles are followed by a spray of buzz droids—parasitic machines that latch onto enemy ships' hulls and drill into crucial systems to render the craft inoperable. Obi-Wan's starfighter is overtaken. As Anakin attempts to scrape the buzz droids off Obi-Wan's hull, one droid manages to attach itself to Anakin's wing. Positioning itself to drill into the systems, the buzz droid exposes its core. R2-D2 quickly enters into battle with the buzz droid. Ever resourceful, R2 uses his electric prod to zap the buzz droid, but the little droid is too quick. Using a tip from Obi-Wan, R2 focuses his attack on the buzz droid's center eye. A direct hit overloads the buzz droid, killing it. The droid slides off the interceptor's wing, saving Anakin's ship and allowing him to continue his mission.

ABOVE: R2-D2 takes out a buzz droid with a direct hit to its center eye.

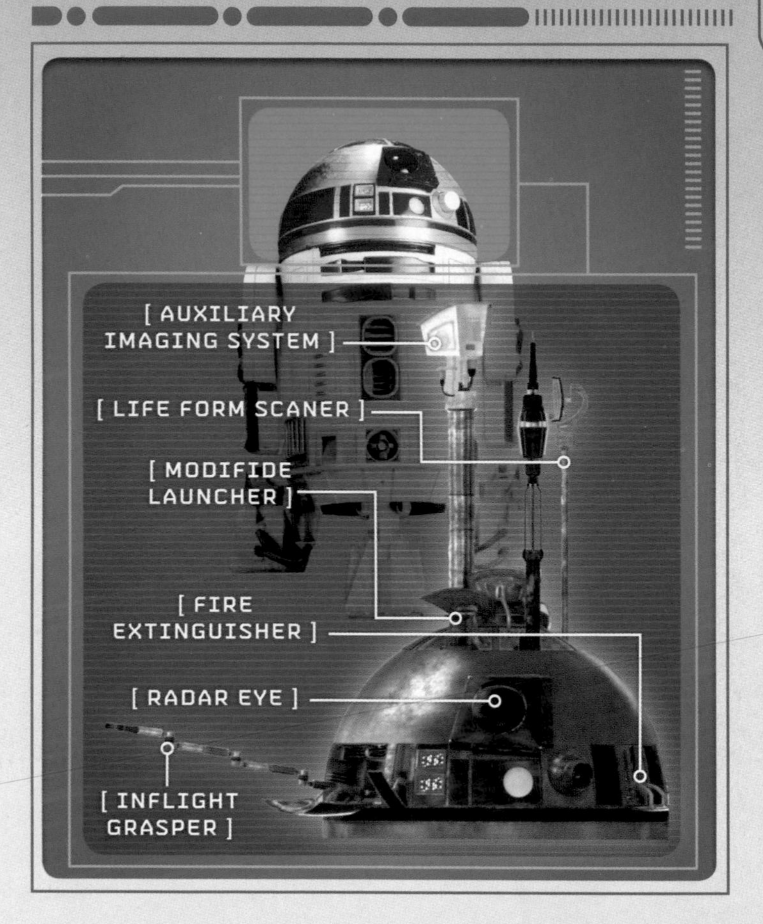

R2-D2's Dome

R2's dome performs many functions, including allowing the droid to see through the use of his photoreceptor. Directly below the photoreceptor is a spotlight that allows the droid to work and move in the dark. The spotlight doubles as a holoprojector through which R2 can deliver holographic messages. Next to the spotlight is R2's status display, which shows how well the droid is working. The dome also contains a periscope—handy for when his body is buried or submerged—a clasper arm, an electric prod that R2 often uses as a weapon, and a scanner antenna.

MINI-MISSION
Locating the Chancellor

LOCATION: **GENERAL GRIEVOUS'S SHIP**

Once the two Jedi Interceptors blast the shields of the *Invisible Hand* and skid into its main hangar bay, R2 jettisons himself from Anakin's ship and braves fire from super battle droids to access a dataport. He uses his universal computer interface arm to plug into the *Invisible Hand*'s systems. Pulling a schematic of the ship and using his holoprojector, he's able to present a layout of the ship for the Jedi. They are able to quickly locate the Chancellor!

HERO NOTES

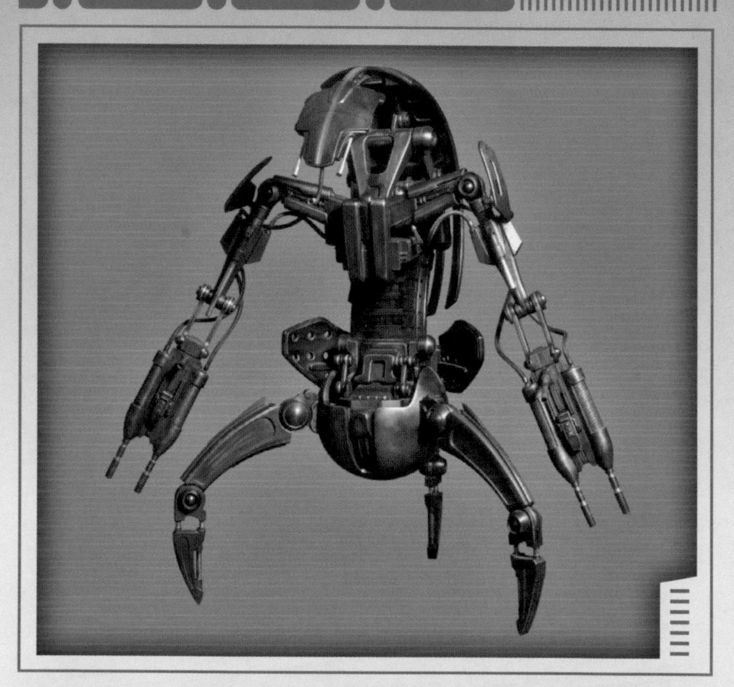

Droidekas

These tripedal droids are also known as destroyer droids, and with good reason. Their shells allow them to curl into a ball and roll over rough terrain, traveling at incredible speeds. They have built-in blaster hands that each fire rounds from two separate tips. But the droids' most dangerous component is the built-in shield generators that render them nearly impossible to destroy.

MISSION 7

SUPER BATTLE DROIDS VS. ASTROMECHS

LOCATION: **GENERAL GRIEVOUS'S SHIP**

As the Jedi take off to rescue the Chancellor, R2 holds his position in the hangar with a comlink in case the Jedi need his help. It isn't too long before Obi-Wan Kenobi contacts him. But the loud voice from the comlink echoes through the empty hangar, drawing the attention of two super battle droids. To avoid their notice, R2 is forced to leave his post, but the urgent need of the Jedi draws R2 back. Bravely, he stands his ground at the dataport, working quickly to assist the Jedi while the super battle droids close in. One picks R2 up and threatens him. R2 showers the droids with oil from his oil-slick arm compartment. Oil splatters everywhere, causing both super battle droids to slip. The one holding R2 trips and lets go of the astromech. Seizing the opportunity, R2 launches his rocket boosters, igniting the oil and frying both super battle droids! R2 flies away to safety and back to work.

ABOVE: R2-D2 faces down two super battle droids.

MISSION 8

DEFEATING GENERAL GRIEVOUS

LOCATION: **GENERAL GRIEVOUS'S SHIP**

The Jedi and R2 succeed in freeing the Chancellor and defeating the Sith Lord Count Dooku in the process. Now they need to escape the *Invisible Hand*—but the mission turns out to be a trap! The Jedi are caught in a ray shield. R2 races to their rescue, but is chased by droidekas. When a wall of super battle droids greets him, R2 shocks them—but it's no use, he's surrounded. R2, the Jedi, and the Chancellor are brought before General Grievous on the bridge of the massive ship. Grievous thinks he has the upper hand, but the Jedi and R2-D2 have another plan. He unleashes a massive assault, firing his electric prod and every other attachment in his arsenal! In the confusion R2 creates, Obi-Wan uses the Force to reclaim his lightsaber from Grievous and cut Anakin free of his shackles. The two fight off several MagnaGuards and battle droids to take control of the ship. Unfortunately, General Grievous escapes, but the Jedi, with the help of R2, bring the Chancellor safely back to Coruscant.

ABOVE: R2-D2 creates a diversion aboard the *Invisible Hand*, giving Obi-Wan and Anakin the chance to escape.

HERO NOTES

Tantive IV

A PROPHETIC ASSIGNMENT

After the downfall of the Republic, Senator Organa, Obi-Wan Kenobi, and Yoda have a final meeting aboard the *Tantive IV*. R2-D2 and C-3PO are assigned to duty aboard *Tantive IV*. C-3PO's memory is wiped as a precaution against him spilling certain secrets, while all involved put faith in R2-D2 to hold their secrets. The two droids remain in service aboard the ship for many years later—until R2-D2 is given a history-changing mission by Princess Leia Organa.

MISSION 9

FINDING OBI-WAN KENOBI

LOCATION: ***TANTIVE IV*, TATOOINE**

As Princess Leia speeds through the Outer Rim on her way to Tatooine, an Imperial Star Destroyer is close on her trail. Princess Leia travels under the banner of a diplomatic mission, but she is actually carrying a set of stolen plans. *Tantive IV* attempts to fend off the Star Destroyer, but is overpowered and boarded by Imperial stormtroopers.

C-3PO and R2-D2, caught in the crossfire, hide in a recessed section of a passage until they can make a break for it. They dash across the hall, dodging laser blasts from both directions.

Defending Rebel forces are quickly defeated, and Darth Vader, Dark Lord of the Sith, boards the ship, intent on retrieving the stolen plans. All personnel aboard the ship—Rebel troops and astromech droids alike—are rounded up by stormtroopers for questioning, but R2 uses his ingenuity and evades them.

Deep in the bowels of the beleaguered craft, Princess Leia and R2-D2 have a clandestine meeting. As R2 records, Princess Leia relays a plea to Jedi Knight Obi-Wan Kenobi, and then feeds the technical readouts of the stolen plans into R2 for safekeeping. C-3PO stumbles upon them just as Leia finishes and slips away.

Following Princess Leia's instruction, R2 heads to the escape pods, goading a fidgety C-3PO to come along. Hesitant, C-3PO warns R2 that they are violating the rules. When R2 tells C-3PO he is heading on a secret mission, C-3PO

LEFT: Princess Leia places the stolen plans in R2-D2.

scoffs, but when stray blaster fire almost destroys them, the whiny protocol droid hurries into the escape pod.

The two jettison from *Tantive IV* and spiral toward Tatooine. They are fortunate that the Imperial troops don't blast them to bits—but as neither droid registers as a life-form aboard the pod, the gunners prefer to conserve power.

Once the escape pod lands, R2-D2 sets off on his mission. C-3PO objects, saying the astromech is going in the wrong direction, but R2 is firm in his belief and heads off toward a rocky area where he believes settlements to be. Once alone, however, he realizes he's being watched. Soon he is ambushed by Jawas—desert-dwelling scavengers who make their livings selling droids and spare parts. They fire an ion blast that shorts his power and incapacitates him. They fit R2 with a restraining bolt and carry him off in their sandcrawler.

As the sandcrawler trundles along the desert, they capture the lost C-3PO—the two droids are reunited! The Jawas stop at the Lars moisture farm where Owen Lars purchases both of them. Owen's nephew, Luke Skywalker, takes the two droids inside to clean them up.

As Luke cleans them, he stumbles across part of Leia's message. R2 refuses to reveal the classified information, so he lies to Luke and tells him it's "old data." When Luke insists that R2 show him the whole message, he tricks Luke into removing the restraining bolt the Jawas placed on him, saying the bolt is

ABOVE: Luke and Uncle Owen purchase droids from the Jawas.

Restraining bolts

In order to keep droids from straying too far, their owners fit them with devices called restraining bolts. Once a restraining bolt is in place, droids can travel only within a radius set by their owners. The device can also be used as a conduit to halt all movements of a droid—as R2 experienced when he tried to follow C-3PO without permission of the Jawas.

HERO | NOTES

R5-D4's Brave Sacrifice

Before buying R2-D2, Owen Lars picks out another droid—an R5 unit named R5-D4. As R5 attempts to follow Luke back to the Lars homestead, his motivator blows up, billowing smoke and causing him to malfunction. C-3PO suggests Luke take R2-D2 instead. If R5 hadn't malfunctioned, R2 would never have met Luke Skywalker and both their futures and that of the galaxy would have been very different.

making it impossible for him to play the entire message. But with the bolt off, R2 still refuses to play any more of the message!

That night, R2 leaves the farm to search for Obi-Wan. R2 doesn't get far when Luke and C-3PO catch up with him. R2 screeches an alert—Sand People are approaching! Luke is ambushed and knocked unconscious, C-3PO is toppled over, but R2 hides himself from the marauders.

A hooded figure approaches, scaring off the Sand People, and checks to make sure Luke is okay. When he notices R2 hiding in the shadows, he calls the droid forward. Shortly afterward Luke regains consciousness and is happy to discover the hooded figure is Obi-Wan Kenobi himself!

Back in safety at Obi-Wan's home, R2 relays the Princess's message, upholding the faith she had placed in him. The Jedi Master asks Luke to join him in completing the next step in the mission and bring the stolen plans to Alderaan.

After some convincing, Luke agrees to go with Obi-Wan to Alderaan and train to be a Jedi Knight.

In seeing this message delivered, R2 accomplishes his bravest and most crucial mission—one that ultimately allows the Rebellion to win its war against the Galactic Empire and helps Luke Skywalker to bring the Jedi Order back into existence.

ABOVE: R2-D2 plays Princess Leia's message for Obi-Wan Kenobi.

MISSION 10

DISCOVERING THE PRINCESS

LOCATION: **DEATH STAR**

To bring the stolen plans to Alderaan, Obi-Wan, Luke, C-3PO, and R2 buy passage aboard the *Millennium Falcon* with Han Solo and Chewbacca as pilots. But instead of Alderaan, the group faces the dreaded Death Star. Though the *Millennium Falcon* is detained, all passengers manage to evade capture. They make their way to a command center where R2 taps into the space station's main computers. He locates the tractor beam that is holding their ship, and Obi-Wan sets off to deactivate it so they can escape.

But that is not the only thing R2 discovers. Beeping excitedly as C-3PO translates, the droid tells them that he's discovered Princess Leia aboard the Death Star. She is being held prisoner and, more gravely, she is scheduled to be terminated! Luke springs into action, asking R2 to locate the Princess's exact location. Thanks to the astromech's ingenuity and resourcefulness, Luke, Han, and Chewbacca are able to infiltrate the detention level and free the Princess from her cell.

ABOVE: Luke, C-3PO, and R2-D2 convince Han Solo to help them rescue Princess Leia.

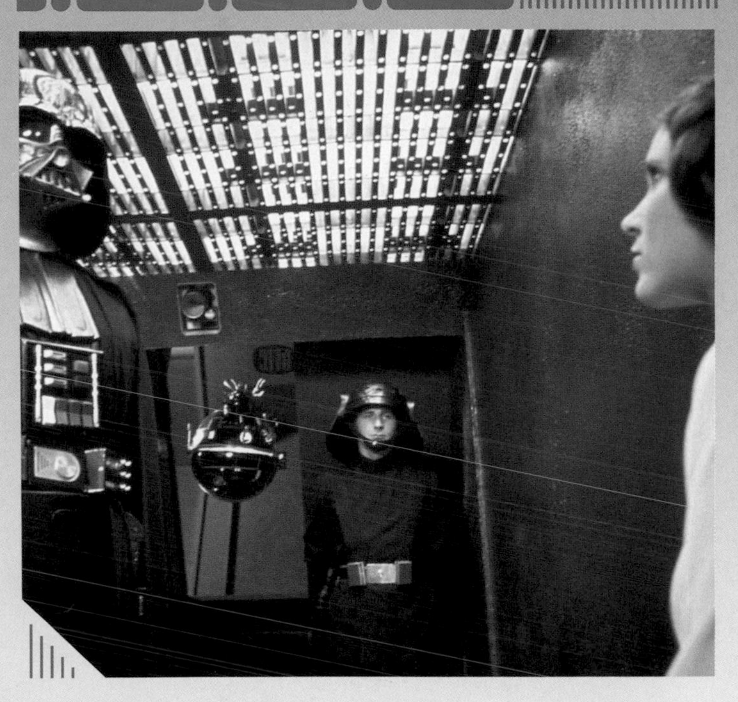

Imperial Droids

There are many droids working on the Death Star—but none are as feared as the interrogator droid, an illegal monster used to administer a truth serum to extract information from prisoners. Princess Leia learns first hand what that experience is like. But true to her nature, she is able to fight off the truth serum's effects.

While interrogator droids are infamous, mouse droids are skittish and cause no threat. They function mainly to transport important messages quickly by zipping through the halls of the Death Star. One mouse droid gets more than it bargains for when it inadvertently approaches Chewbacca. The Wookiee lets out a roar that sends the timid droid zooming in the other direction!

HERO **NOTES**

R2's Core

R2-D2's cylindrical body contains several compartments that house the components astromech droids use for their daily tasks, such as repair tools and interface arms. His body has two main legs on each side, and one retractable leg that extends when needed. Along with compartments and arms, R2's main body is equipped with many ports and sockets that allow him to interface with devices and other computers as well as recharge or run diagnostics. In addition to tools and ports, his body includes a cargo compartment for storage and ventilation ports to keep his systems running properly.

MISSION 11

RESCUING THE HEROES

LOCATION: **DEATH STAR**

Princess Leia is free, but in order to evade stormtroopers, the heroes are forced to crawl into a trash chute, which dumps them into a trash compactor. The Imperials figure out their escape and activate the trash compactor. The heroes have nowhere to go when the walls begin to close in on them. They frantically try to call R2-D2 so he can turn the compactor off.

But R2 and C-3PO are having troubles of their own. Stormtroopers rush in and take over the command center. The droids manage to escape and make their way to the hangar bay where the *Millennium Falcon* is being held. There, C-3PO wonders how the others are doing. R2 tells him to check using the comlink Luke gave him. C-3PO finally contacts Luke, who frantically screams at him to shut down the trash compactor.

C-3PO relays the message to R2, who takes control of the situation. He immediately plugs into the Death Star's systems and shuts down all the trash compactors on the detention level. He then unlocks the magnetically sealed door, allowing the heroes to avoid a hideous end!

ABOVE: R2-D2 links into the Death Star's central computer to shut down the trash compactor.

MISSION 12

DESTROYING THE DEATH STAR

LOCATION: **DEATH STAR / PLANET YAVIN SPACE**

All the heroes except Obi-Wan Kenobi escape the Death Star and eventually make their way to the Rebel Alliance base. There R2-D2 is finally able to share the stolen plans he's been harboring. He plugs into the Rebel Alliance's computers and uploads the Death Star's blueprints. Rebel leaders analyze the plans and find a small but potentially deadly weakness in the Death Star defenses. However, it requires small, single-troop fighters to maneuver the space station's equatorial trench and fire a proton torpedo into its exhaust port.

It's a slim chance, but the Rebels must take it, for when the heroes escaped, Imperial forces followed them—the Death Star is moving into position to use its superweapon to destroy the Rebel base and the planet upon which it is located. The Rebels scramble to get their troops together and launch their attack on the battle station.

Luke Skywalker volunteers to pilot an X-wing fighter in the battle against the Death Star. X-wings require an astromech copilot, and Luke won't even consider going into battle without R2. Through all their adventures, the two have become partners.

R2's assistance is invaluable as Luke battles numerous TIE fighters in his attempts to get to the equatorial trench and start his attack run. R2 diligently performs emergency repairs to Luke's X-wing, boosting power and locking down loose components.

As Luke makes his final approach to the exhaust port, Darth Vader—piloting a TIE fighter—fires on Luke's X-wing. The shot is a direct hit on R2's dome. The droid lets out a sad shriek before all his systems completely short out.

Sadly, R2 isn't conscious to witness the outcome of the battle, but once he's repaired, the droid is ecstatic to discover that Luke destroyed the Death Star and saved the Rebellion—all with his help!

MINI-MISSION
Detecting Luke

LOCATION: **HOTH**

Following the battle with the Death Star, both Luke and Han join the Rebel forces. On a routine check of the Alliance's new base on the ice plant Hoth, Luke goes missing. Han Solo rashly heads out in the freezing conditions to find Luke. When neither of them return, R2 worries. He stands by the entrance to the Rebels' secret base using all his equipment to run a continuous search for any life-forms. R2 isn't able to locate Han or Luke before the leaders insist on closing the shield doors. With heavy beeps, R2 tells Princess Leia the chances of survival in the extreme temperatures are 725 to one. C-3PO translates, but adds, "Actually, R2 has been known to make mistakes. From time to time."

HERO NOTES

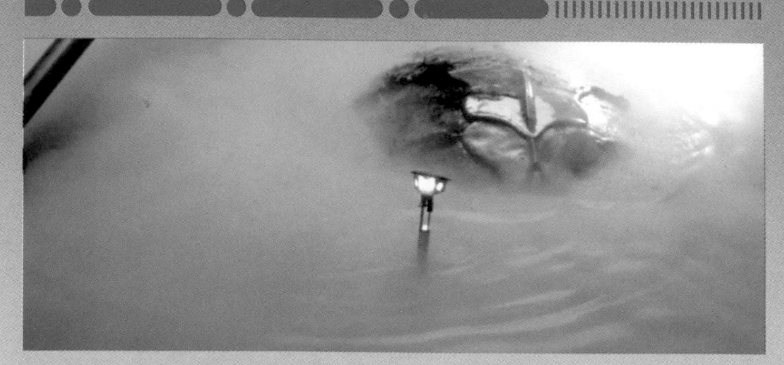

R2 Is Eaten

As Luke puts it, "You're lucky droids don't taste very good." When trying to make it to dry land after landing in a swamp on Dagobah, R2 topples from Luke's X-wing and splashes into the water. He uses his periscope photoreceptor in his dome to see above the water and navigate to land. All is going well—until a massive swamp creature swallows R2 whole! The beast soon discovers R2 isn't a creature, but a droid. It spits R2 out, shooting him across the swamp onto land. Lucky for R2, nothing is broken!

MINI-MISSION
Retrieving the Lamp

LOCATION: **DAGOBAH**

Luke and R2 head to the Dagobah system in search of the last remaining Jedi Master, a mysterious being named Yoda. After a crash into a swamp, they set up camp on a patch of land. To their surprise, a giggling green creature appears and starts asking Luke questions. Luke, annoyed by the creature, tries to ignore him—but the being makes it difficult when he starts rooting through Luke's belongings and scattering them around. When the creature finds a tiny lamp, he cackles excitedly and refuses to give it back. R2 very sneakily extends his grasping arm and latches onto the lamp. He and the being get into a struggle over the lamp, but Luke finally relents, telling R2 to let it go. R2 reluctantly releases his grip on the lamp, only to receive a nasty smack from the being! Later, both R2 and Luke are surprised to discover that R2 had fought with a Jedi Master!

HERO | NOTES

R2's Arm Extensions

Each of the extendable devices held in R2's chest and dome is designed to perform different tasks, from sawing to welding to gathering information. His most important appendage by far is his universal computer interface arm, which he uses to get information from and talk to computer systems across the galaxy. Second to his interface arm is his multifunction utility and interface arm, which he uses to make emergency repairs.

MISSION 13

RESCUE IN THE CLOUDS

LOCATION: **BESPIN**

While on Dagobah, Luke has a vision of his friends in trouble. Luke and R2 leave for Cloud City. Once they land, he and R2 are quickly separated. R2 searches the city and comes across Chewbacca, Leia, and Lando Calrissian.

Strapped to Chewbacca's back is C-3PO—who is in several pieces! R2 joins his friends, and as they race through the city's halls C-3PO fills him in on what is happening: they are desperately trying to save Han Solo who is being taken away by a bounty hunter! The heroes reach the landing platforms too late—the ship carrying Solo blasts off. The heroes rush back through Cloud City in a desperate attempt to board the *Millennium Falcon*.

The doors to where the *Falcon* is parked are shut. R2 steps forward and gets the doors to the platform open just as Imperial troops arrive and open fire. R2 holds off the stormtroopers by unleashing blasts from his fire extinguisher and blanketing the entrance to the platform in a thick spray of flame retardant.

R2 wheels through the haze as Leia and Lando fight off troops, allowing everyone to get aboard the *Falcon* and blast away from Cloud City.

ABOVE: R2-D2 holds off stormtroopers with a well timed blast from his fire extinguisher.

MISSION 14

ESCAPING CLOUD CITY

LOCATION: **BESPIN**

As the *Millennium Falcon* zooms away from Cloud City, they realize the hyperdrive is not working. Without it, they'll be captured! Chewbacca leaps out of his seat and starts to work on it.

C-3PO is still in several pieces, so R2-D2 sets to work putting his friend back together. It is while R2 is busy fixing C-3PO that he hears about the hyperdrive. He tells C-3PO the hyperdrive is not broken. Cloud City's central computer told him it had been deactivated. Chewbacca is working in the wrong place. Only R2 knows what to do to get the hyperdrive working again!

R2 races to a terminal, and with his multifunction utility and interface arm, he reactivates the ship's hyperdrive just in time for the *Falcon* to avoid being caught. R2 and the rest of the Rebels blast into hyperspace, away from Cloud City and the Empire.

ABOVE: R2-D2 puts his friend C-3PO back together once again.

MISSION 15

LIBERATING HAN SOLO

LOCATION: **TATOOINE**

R2-D2 and C-3PO enter Jabba's palace to deliver a message to the Hutt crime lord as part of a plan to rescue Han Solo, who was being held prisoner after being delivered by the bounty hunter Boba Fett. Only R2 has been entrusted with the full scope of the plan to rescue Solo––everyone knows C-3PO couldn't handle the information or face the danger as calmly as R2. When R2-D2 and C-3PO are brought before the Hutt's dais, R2 delivers a holographic message from Luke Skywalker—who offers the two droids a token of Luke's goodwill! When the message finishes playing, Jabba scoffs. He won't give up Han Solo, but he will definitely keep the droids.

R2 and C-3PO are dragged into the bowels of Jabba's palace, where they are fitted with restraining bolts. R2 is then assigned to Jabba's sail barge, where he serves drinks and performs other menial tasks. In the meantime, Leia and Chewbacca, also part of Luke's plan, make their way to the crime lord's palace.

Despite their best efforts, the Rebels are all taken captive and are scheduled to pay the ultimate penalty: They are going to be thrown into a giant pit where a sarlacc beast will slowly devour them. Although it seems like the end, R2 maneuvers himself into position at the edge of Jabba's sail barge and waits for Luke's signal.

A guard shoves Luke into position above the sarlacc's gaping maw. It's then that the Jedi motions to R2, who jettisons a lightsaber from a secret chamber in his dome, launching it right into Luke's hand! Luke ignites the weapon, freeing Chewbacca and Han.

While Luke battles to free his friends outside, it is left to R2 to help Leia aboard the sail barge. She is chained to Jabba himself. Using another of his arms, R2 cuts through her shackles and Leia joins the others in the fight.

As the battle nears an end, R2-D2 comes across a beleaguered C-3PO—Jabba's pet, Salacious Crumb, has ripped out C-3PO's eye. R2 shocks the creature, scaring him off. R2 and C-3PO move to the edge of the barge, but it's a long drop! R2 shoves his friend off the edge of the ship and then jumps overboard himself.

Han Solo is safe and the Rebels leave to continue their struggle against the Empire—the plan succeeded and R2-D2 came through for his friends once again.

ABOVE: R2-D2 and C-3PO deliver Luke's message to Jabba the Hutt.

HERO NOTES

Droids in Jabba's Palace

Droids in Jabba's palace have a hard road. They all report to a supervisor droid, EV-9D9. Her programming makes her sadistic and ruthless. EV-9D9 does not hesitate to torture or even disintegrate fellow droids if they fail to live up to her expectations. It is a lesson R2-D2 narrowly avoids learning when he sasses her, and she warns him to learn some respect if he wants to stay in one piece.

MINI-MISSION
Escaping the Net

LOCATION: **FOREST MOON OF ENDOR**

As the galaxy faces the threat of a second Death Star, a Rebel squad travels to the Forest Moon of Endor. Princess Leia is soon separated from the group, so R2 and the other heroes search the forest for any signs of her. R2's scanners are vital in their search. He tries desperately to pick up any signals that will point to her whereabouts. Chewbacca picks up a scent—but it isn't Leia. It's a dead animal. Luke yells at him not to touch it, but Chewie grabs the carcass, triggering a trap that ensnares all the Rebel heroes in a giant net. Suspended midair, barely able to move, R2-D2 comes to their rescue once again. Extending his utility saw, he cuts through the ropes holding them and they all fall to the forest ground below.

HERO | NOTES

The Third Leg

For faster and smoother mobility over various types of terrain, astromech droids are equipped with a retractable third leg that rests within their cylindrical bodies. When the need arises, astromechs can extend their third leg and tilt their bodies back slightly. The three legs provide greater stability, and the additional tread provides greater speed.

MISSION 16

THE FINAL BATTLE

LOCATION: **FOREST MOON OF ENDOR**

The Rebels are in a desperate race to deactivate the shield protecting the second Death Star, which is under construction above the planet's atmosphere. In order to do so, they must break into a bunker located on the moon's surface.

Princess Leia and Han Solo secured a code that should open the bunker's hatch, but the code has been changed. Leia calls for R2, hoping he can override the security system and break the code. To reach her, R2 must race between blasterfire across uneven terrain. He sets off without a second thought, with C-3PO trailing behind, whining the entire way. Once the two arrive at the bunker, R2 plugs into the console and attempts to unlock the doors. But while he works on the door, his body is exposed to the battle. A stray shot is a direct hit! R2 short-circuits—all his panels and wiring violently surge as smoke pours out of him.

ABOVE: A direct hit overloads R2-D2's circuits.

Han eventually manages to finish what R2-D2 started. The Rebels get the door open and manage to blow up the shield generator. Lando Calrissian, leading the attack above the planet, is able to destroy the Death Star.

As the Rebels regroup on Endor and news of the Empire's defeat spreads, a galaxy-wide celebration breaks out. Planet after planet joins in the victory cry, toppling statues of their fallen dictators and cheering.

Once R2-D2 recovers from his jolt, he joins the friends he's fought alongside through so many desperate battles and claims his place as a true hero of the galaxy.

ABOVE: R2-D2 and the rest of the heroes regroup to celebrate the destruction of the Death Star and the Empire.